Public Health in Crisis

Confined in the
Aegean Archipelago

kyklàda.press

first published by kyklàda.press in
2020, this book is the second edition,
published in 2021. kyklàda.press is an
imprint of PHOTOGRAPHIC
EXPANDED PUBLISHING ATHENS.

978-9-464202-87-8
D/2021/15058/02

@kyklada.press
www.kyklada.press

Impending Arrivals
Dimitra Kondylatou
& David Bergé

Cruises to Nowhere

When in March 2020, Covid-19 hit the ocean liner MS Zaandam, the ship and her passengers found themselves stranded off the coast of Chile somewhere in the Pacific Ocean. After several ports refused to let MS Zaandam dock, her sister ship Rotterdam was sent with medical backup and supplies and both continued towards Florida. With a sick toll running up to 148, MS Zaandam was initially denied transit through the Panama Canal. While the ship waited to be granted permission to enter, four passengers died. Despite the pleas of the cruise company's president, Orlando Ashford, for "compassion and grace"[1] the local governors, already overwhelmed with the health management in their own countries, kept rejecting the ship's requests to dock.

"Compassion and grace." Hearing this, we can not help thinking of the hundreds of refugees in the Mediterranean Sea who, after crossing help-lessly on rescue boats, are denied entry at European ports and get pushed back, even capsized, by European coast guards. In the case of MS Zaandam, the British, American and Australian holidaymakers onboard, finally found their way home via chartered flights.

MS Zaandam was not the only cruise ship to be left adrift carrying coronavirus patients. There is a long list of other cruise ships trapped at sea. This fact has left the cruise industry shaken, thrown off course by the pandemic, perhaps more than any other travel industry.

In an attempt to generate revenue for the sector and regain passengers' confidence in the industry, Singapore launched 'Cruises to Nowhere'[2] —a cruise experience without stops. With extra precautions and carrying passengers at half of its capacity, World Dream of Genting Cruise Lines will be the first 'Cruise to Nowhere' on 6 November 2020. Passengers will be encouraged to stay in their air-conditioned cabins, wear masks in all common areas, and will be discouraged from meeting other people on board. In a similar spirit, Qantas Airline —having grounded most international flights since the beginning of the pandemic—put in place a seven hour long flight around Australia's landmarks with no destination. This novelty emphasizes the act of traveling over reaching a destination. As such it has been met with hostile reactions from environ-mental groups and activists, as the cruise industry is one of the most polluting leisure industries.

These articles made us wonder why in the context of physical and social distancing people are interested in traveling for the sake of traveling, and why this might seem, or be, pleasurable.

Covid-19 stricken Ships

World Dream
Diamond Princess
Grand Princess
River Anuket
Costa Magica
Breamar
Costa Luminosa
Silver Explorer
Silver Shadow
Norwegian Bliss
Norwegian Breakaway
Celebrity Solstice
Ruby Princess
MSC Bellissima
Ovation of the Seas
Voyager of the Seas
Costa Victoria
Artania
Celebrity Apex
Costa Favolosa
MSC Splendida
Sun Princess
MS Zaandam
MS Rotterdam (renamed as Borealis
in August 2020)
Horizon
Oasis of the Seas
Liberty of the Seas

Coral Princess
Disney Wonder
Greg Mortimer
Pride of America
Celebrity Flora
Monarch
Costa Atlantica
MSC Seaview
Mein Schiff 3
MSC Preziosa
Seven Seas Navigator
Adventure of the Seas
Mein Schiff 1
Roald Anundsen
MS Paul Gauguin

Images and representations of contaminated ships, adrift or docked in harbors, have existed for a long time as diseases have been and continue to be often spread through travel. The previous millennium faced multiple, frequent and consistent virus attacks. The scale, the intensity of the disease, and the speed of its spread is what determines whether it is considered an outbreak, an epidemic or a pandemic. In terms of geography, pandemics travel faster and know no borders. One of the most severe and persistent pandemics, coming to Europe in three waves, was the Plague. During the second wave, known as the Black Death due to its severeness and fatality, the plague was often carried via sea as maritime commerce was developing at a fast pace. Frank Snowden remarks in *Epidemics and Society* that:

> "Infected rats climbed aboard ships via ropes and gangplanks and were lifted aboard in crates of wheat and rice. In this way, shipping was essential to the spread of Plague over long distances; this helps to explain the epidemiology of the disease — that is, its tendency to arrive in a country by ship and then to move inland by road and river traffic. For the black rat, the Mediterranean was not a barrier but a highway. Istanbul (known as Constantinople between 330 and 1453) was a vital hub of

trade and disease. It linked the whole of the Mediterranean—overland via the Balkans and by sea to Venice, Naples, Corfu, Genoa, Marseille and Valencia. Sometimes, there was havoc at sea, when the Plague destroyed entire crews, and ghost ships drifted on the waves. More frequently, however, a ship would dock, and its cargo of rats would disembark via the same hoists, ropes and gangplanks that had first brought them aboard."[3]

Dimitra Kondylatou is a visual artist living in Athens. Through moving-image, editing, writing, and hosting, she explores art's entanglements with tourism and everyday life.

David Bergé is an artist living in Athens and Brussels. He works with site-specific interventions, installations, Walk Pieces, and book projects.

1. Greenfield, Patrick and McCormick, Erin. "Cruise operator says lives are at risk on Zaandam as nations 'turn their backs' on ship." The Guardian, March 31, 2020.

2. McMahon, Shannon. "First came flights to nowhere during the pandemic. Cruises to nowhere may be next." The Washington Post, October 1, 2020.

3. Snowden, Frank. Epidemics and Society: From the Black Death to the Present. New Heaven; London: Yale University Press, 2019. p. 43

Suspended Arrivals
Dimitra Kondylatou
&David Bergé

Le Corbusier Confined

(...) Here is Attica, and there is the Peloponnesus. Here is a white lighthouse and, very near, a harbor. Here are unusually jagged hills, little resembling those of Broussa or the ones behind Scutari. The sea is deserted. At this moment of dawn there are none of the countless longboats laden with carpous, tomatoes, and vegetables, which, as in Constantinople, are heading toward the city with the clumsy haste of big beetles. This brown land seems a desert. Very far away in the center of the harbor, at the bosom of some hills forming an arch, a strange rock stands out, flat at the top and secured on its right by a yellow cube. The Parthenon and the Acropolis! But we cannot believe it; we don't give it a thought. We are bewildered; the ship does not enter the harbor but continues on its course.

The symbolic rock disappears, hidden by a promontory. The sea is extremely narrow; we pass around an island. Oh, damn! Ten, twenty ships are anchored there, each flying a yellow flag! The flag of cholera, that of the Kavas; from the Black Sea to Tuzla on the Marmara. That flag we know indeed! The propeller suddenly becomes silent. The anchors drop. We stop. The yellow flag is hoisted. Stupefaction! A great stir, general restlessness. The captain is nervous, becomes violent, shouts, insults: "The longboats are in the water. Passengers for Athens, come on, get moving!" Chaos. Bundles and boxes, men and women, come clattering down the ladder. Such cries, such insults, such shouting, and in every language. On a small pier toward which the oarsmen steer us is a gentleman with a white cap, servile with the rich, brutal and rude with the poor: a functionary, a penpusher! Wire fences separate the barracks. The quarantine!

— Charles-Édouard Jeanneret,
the future Le Corbusier,
excerpt from diary (1911).

Quarantine took its name from the Italian word *quarantina*, meaning 'about forty' and originally referring to the period of confinement put in place as a measure against the Plague Epidemic in 14th-century Venice. The origin of this temporary isolation comes from Christianity. In both the *Old* and *New Testament* there is the suggestion that 40 is the threshold at which purification is reached: 40 days is the length of Moses's isolation on Mount Sinai receiving the Ten Commandments; 40 days of Christ's temptation; 40 days and nights of the flood in Genesis; and Christ stays with his disciples for 40 days after his resurrection. At the outbreak of the Plague, it seemed more effective to provide spiritual comfort to an anxious city than a scientific framework. Forty days was, in fact, enough time to kill infected fleas and plague bacteria by exposure to sun and air. It also exceeded the incubation period of the Plague.

The Plague first appeared in Europe around the middle of the 6th century. It lasted for almost two centuries and mortality rates were dreadful. In 1347 it reappeared aboard Genoese galleys that had sailed from the Black sea to the Sicilian port of Messina. It spread through Sardinia and Corsica, first to Italy and then to the rest of Europe. Within the next five years, across multiple waves, the Plague, also known as the Black Death, had killed more than five million people—almost one third of the population

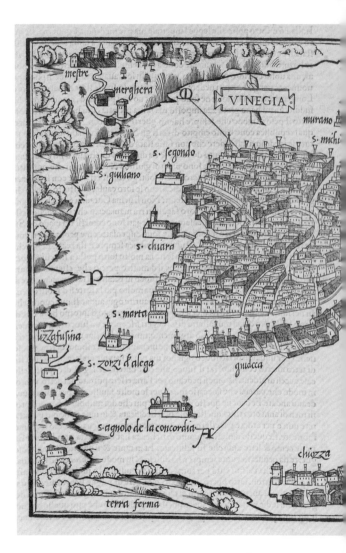

mestre

merghera

VINEGIA

murano

s. michi

s. segondo

s. giuliano

s. chiara

s. marta

lizZafusina

s. zorzi d'alega

guidecca

s. agnolo de la concordia

chiozza

terra ferma

Fig. 1
Map of Venice and surrounding islands, 1528.

of Europe at that time. Since the 13th-century, Europe had faced an economic recession. Urbanization, population growth concurrent with insufficient housing and harsh weather conditions, led to what is known as the medieval *Great Famine* (lasting from 1315 to 1322). The poor living conditions evoked fragile public health and inevitably contributed to the endemicity and severe fatality of the Plague.

Aware of its vulnerability as a city with one of the most important and frequently visited commercial ports, Venice was one of the first cities to take preventive measures to protect itself. Between 1361 and 1528, the city recorded 22 Plague outbreaks. Citizens were confined to their houses, and the whole city was arranged as a large enclosed space with contained foldings. Before entering the city, travelers were confined inside contaminated or suspect ships, and in *lazarettos*—quarantine stations especially built for sanitary control, usually located on islets or remote areas close to harbors. In order to constrict the arrival and the spread of the Plague, the Office of Health in Venice organized lazarettos, quarantine periods and Sanitary Cordons. Two large institutions, *Lazzaretto Vecchio* and *Lazzaretto Nuovo*, were established on isolated islands in the Lagoon in which arriving ships were commanded to dock.

Vessels from suspected areas were held to be scrubbed and fumigated. Crew and passengers, consisting of hundreds of people, were often unwilling to come to shore as they were confined and isolated for 40 days. Cargo and all personal items were offloaded, exposed to the sun, fumigated and aired. After 40 days, goods and passengers were released to continue into Venice or to their next stops. Many of these purification rituals did not have any effect except for paving the path for a more authoritarian state and the justification of military presence. Other European ports such as Marseille, Corfu, Valencia, Genoa, Naples, Amsterdam and Rotterdam copied the Venetian confinement strategy and built their own lazarettos.

Lazzaretto took its name from one of two possible sources. The first is an alliteration of Santa Maria di Nazaret, the island that hosted the first such structure. The second is from the parable of Lazarus the beggar. Before lazarettos became landmarks of public health, lepers were isolated in houses, areas and islands called *lazar houses* as administered by Christian religious orders. As well as being used as a name for lepers, the term *lazar* was broadly used to name the ill, the beggars, the poor, the homeless, the 'unclean' and marginal figures.

Anoyatis-Pelé, Dimitrios, Athanasopoulou, Ioanna and Tsiamis, Costas. "Cartographic Heritage in the Historical Study of Public Health: The Case of Mediterranean Lazzaretos." In e-Perimetron 11, no.1 (2016): 35-46.

Cliff, Andrew, Smallman-Raynor, Matthew and Stevens, Peta. "Controlling the Geographical Spread of Infectious Disease: plague in Italy, 1347-1851." In Acta medico-historica adriatica: AMHA 7, no. 2 (2009): 197-236.

Snowden, Frank. Epidemics and Society: From the Black Death to the Present. New Haven; London: Yale University Press, 2019.

Žaknić, Ivan. Journey to the East / Le Corbusier (Charles-Édouard Jeanneret), edited and annotated by Ivan Žaknić. Translated by Ivan Žaknić in collaboration with Nicole Pertuiset. Cambridge, Massachusetts: MIT Press, 1987.

Confined Spaces
Dimitra Kondylatou

Religious and Medical Approaches to the Plague

Mary Douglas offered a structural analysis of 'purity and pollution', by taking into account a wider range of social systems and chronologies with different logics and symbolic interpretations. She wrote: "If we can abstract pathogenicity and hygiene from our notion of dirt, we are left with the old definition of dirt as matter out of place." (Douglas, 1980). By this, she suggested that dirt is always inherently bound to a social system. "Dirt is the by-product of a systematic ordering and classification of matter, in so far as ordering involves rejecting inappropriate elements. This idea of dirt takes us straight into the field of symbolism and promises a link-up with more obviously symbolic systems of purity." (Douglas, 1980).

In Medieval Europe, the perception of 'the miasmatic' was heavily influenced by religious interpretations of physical or mental illness as divine punishment for immoral, sinful and unfaithful behavior. Purity came through spiritual catharsis and repentance. While medical science was not yet developed to understand the nature and the mechanisms of the disease fully—bacteria would not be identified as agents of disease until the 1880s—it was popular imagination that dealt with contagion the most. Religion, parareligion and superstition offered remedies against the Plague that however did not guarantee cure from it. Prayers, religious amulets and talismans were put in practice against terror and fear caused by the lack of knowledge from the invisible threat.

Often enough, the cleansing measures suggested by doctors coincided with religious purification symbolisms. Water, for instance, besides its literal and practical use for cleaning, had a symbolic meaning deriving from baptism as a ritual for the purification of the soul. Similarly, fire and smoke suggested for fumigation, acquired a symbolic character and a larger dimension. People burnt herbs and sulfur, suggested by doctors as disinfectants, but they would burn them in bonfires, to exorcise evil. Therefore cleansing methods were put in practice by the majority of people rather for religious than for sanitary reasons.

Since the 14th century and until the 19th, doctors, physicians, care-takers, priests and those who would get in contact with Plague victims, wore specially designed protective wear made of leather and waxed fabric; and masks with nose-extensions filled with aromatic herbs to infiltrate the air from the polluted and dangerous smells.

The ongoing medical research was leading faster to conclusions for the advancement and enhancement of prevention methods against the spread of the disease; rather than to its cure. It constantly redefined changes in the quarantine duration, the cleansing methods and the ingredients used for the fumigation of goods, merchandise and personal possessions of citizens, confined to their houses; as well as passing-by travelers, confined to ships and lazarettos. Prevention methods were organized and secured by special boards, committees and administrators.

Public Health and Public Order

The symbolic systems of purity suggested by Mary Douglas can be linked with the idea of dirt as a by-product of a systematic ordering through social and spatial, non-metaphysical, forms. The association of order with cleanliness is besides a religious, also a social perception put into practice by the state and by individuals, both in previous times and contemporary societies. People, areas, objects, jobs that are being considered 'dirty' are stigmatized and sometimes dislocated, isolated and socially excluded for being a menace to the 'proper and moral society'.

Fig. 2
Prayers and religious motifs put in practice against
the fear caused by the Plague, Medieval etching.

Illness, except for the consequences it has on the individual body and the health of the population, causes a disorder in the life of the city, of the society, the globe, depending on the size of the pandemic. It affects the way people think, behave and act in the everyday, and the way they envision the future. It affects their personal relationships. In the presence of a virus, the mixing together of freely moving bodies is considered dangerous. The survival of society is a matter of good planning that defines a safe model behavior for the citizens. So far, in most cities, this is achieved through the orchestrated action of the medical, the administrative and the penal systems, according to which the emphasis is being put, instead of medical enhancement and care, on policing and surveillance.

In *Illness as Metaphor* Susan Sontag associated health with politics, on the basis of regularity: "Order is the oldest concern of political philosophy, and if it is plausible to compare the polis to an organism, then it is plausible to compare civil disorder to an illness. The classical formulations which analogize a political disorder to illness—from Plato to, say, Hobbes—presuppose the classical medical (and political) idea of balance. Illness comes from imbalance. Treatment is aimed at restoring the right balance—in political terms, the right hierarchy. The prognosis is always, in principle, optimistic. Society, by definition, never catches a fatal disease." (Sontag, 1978). Douglas, being preoccupied with the spatial treatment of those elements pointed out by normative societies as 'inappropriate', visualized the sturdiness of society as follows: "The idea of society is a powerful image. It is potent in its own right to control or to stir men to action. This image has form; it has external boundaries, margins, internal structure. Its outlines contain the power to reward conformity and repulse attack." (Douglas, 1980). The outlines, the boundaries of society, have the power to arrange and to secure and define spaces within and outside them.

Michel Foucault often reflected on strictly outlined spaces functioning as operators for the restoration of order. In *Discipline and Punish: The birth of prison* his description of the Plague-stricken town of the 17th century as "an enclosed, segmented space, observed at every point, in which the individuals are inserted in a fixed place, in which the slightest movements are supervised, in which all events are recorded, in which an uninterrupted work of writing links the center and periphery, in which power is exercised without division, according to a continuous hierarchical figure, in which each individual is constantly located, examined and distributed among the living beings, the sick and the dead" (Foucault, 1980), shows how the spatial arrangement delivered the biopolitics of the everyday life of the individual. It defined where they stayed, and for how long, how they moved, how they lived, how they died and where.

The exact details of a life lived in a confined city can be found in Daniel Defoe's *Journal of the*

Plague Year (2001). Defoe used words such as misery, terror and desperation for the confined, lamentation, grief and mourning for the ones that had losses, but also severity, cruelty and violence, as there were some incidents of resistance in the form of escapes from the closed houses that turned into prisons for their owners. The deceased were buried in massive graves, in churchyards, which living people were not allowed to approach, and in which the sick and desperate wanted to throw themselves into. Among his notes and observations, he cited the "Orders Conceived and Published by the Lord Mayor and Aldermen of the City of London Concerning the Infection of the Plague in 1665." This citation reveals how several roles and responsibilities were hierarchically appointed to secure the right application of these orders. Specific positions, such as the examiners, the watchmen, the searchers, the surgeons and the nurse-keepers, were given specific tasks, according to their status, gender and capacity, in the treatment of the disease or the surveillance of the confined residents. Moreover, specific regulations defined the everyday life in the city, concerning not only the management of the disease but also the inhabitation of houses, the social life and human relationships and the life in the street. In the Plague-stricken city, all festivities and gatherings were banned, people were forbidden to go to taverns, restaurants and coffee shops after nine in the evening, homeless people would disappear from the streets and stray animals were being killed.

The lazaretto offers another example on the association of spatial arrangement with pathogenicity and hygiene. The organization of the confined city as a surveillance mechanism set the grounds for the structural form of lazarettos.

Architectures of Control

> Behind the disciplinary mechanisms can be read the haunting memory of 'contagions', of the Plague, of rebellions, crimes, vagabondage, desertions, people who appear and disappear, live and die in disorder.
> — Michel Foucault, *Discipline and Punish: The birth of the prison* (1995)

John Howard was an early English prison reformer. His work focused on the enhancement of the physical and mental health of the prisoners, including the administration of security and order. Departing from that aspect, he observed many similarities between the living conditions in prison and in lazarettos, during his *Grand Tour* journey in 1748. In *An account of the Principal Lazarettos in Europa* (1791) his proposal for a new plan for *lazarettos* resembled his recommendations for the prison enhancement, aiming at a better life quality for the inmates and better rules for maintaining the health standards. In his words "Many lazarettos are closed, and have too much the aspect of prisons; and I have often heard captains in the Levant trade say that the spi-

Fig. 3
Illustration of a physician wearing a 17th-century
Plague preventive costume.

Fig. 4

Fig. 4
Franciscan monks treating victims of the Plague in Perugia,
Italy, 16th century.

Fig. 5
Page from Fasciculus medicine,
a medical manual printed in Venice, 1495.

The Manner of Dissecting
the

PESTILENTIALL BODY.

Printed for Nath: Crouch at the Rose and Crowne in Exchang Alle

Fig. 6

ΛΟΙΜΟΤΟΜΙΑ:
OR THE
PEST Anatomized

In these following particulars, *Viz.*

1. *The Material Cause*
2. *The Efficient Cause* } of the PEST,
3. *The Subject Part*
4. *The Signs*
5. *An Historical Account of the Dissection of a Pestilential Body by the Author; and the Consequents thereof.*
6. *Reflections and Observations on the foresaid Dissection.*
7. *Directions Preservative and Curative against the Pest.*

Together with the *Authors Apology* against the Calumnies of the *Galenists:* and a Word to Mr. *Nath: Hodges,* concerning his late *Vindiciæ Medicinæ.*

By *George Thomson*, M. D.

Ουκ δικτίεον ὑπὸ τῆ λοιμῶ τε εἶναι @ ἀλλὰ τῆς ψυχῆς ὃ ἐστιν ἀγνοίας ἀπαλλαγῆναι.

Diis talem terris avertite Pestem.

London, Printed for *Nath: Crouch,* at the *Rose* and *Crown* in *Exchange-*Alley near *Lombard-street;* 1 6 6 6

2
8

Fig. 7

Fig. 8

Fig. 6
Two men dissecting a plague infected body, line engraving, 1666.
Fig. 7
A yellow quarantine flag raised on a ship anchored at sea,
20th-century watercolor.
Fig. 8
Convicts cleansing and disinfecting infected buildings,
ink drawing, 1891.

Fig. 9

Fig. 10

Fig. 9-10
Illustration of a physician wearing 17th-century
Plague preventive costumes.

Fig. 11
Fatal diseases attributed to rats in Marseille,
color lithograph, 1920.

Fig. 12

Fig. 13

Fig. 12
Plague apparatus for the disinfection of clothing
from a lazaretto in Venice.

Fig. 13
Plague apparatus for the disinfection of letters and papers
from a lazaretto in Venice.

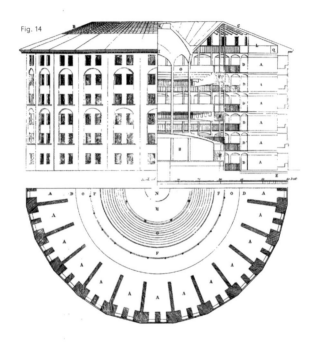

Fig. 14

Fig. 15, 16

Fig. 14
Panopticon: the ubiquitous system of institutional surveillance
conceived by the English philosopher and social theorist Jeremy
Bentham in the 18th-century. Architectural drawing, 1791.

Fig. 15
The lazaretto at Syros, drawing, 1867.

Fig. 16
View of Ermoupolis, the capital of Syros, watercolor, 1838.

Fig. 17
Ermoupolis as seen from inside the lazaretto,
Syros, video still, 2020.

Fig. 18
Passengers undergoing quarantine examination
on a docked ship, 1883.

rits of their passengers sink at the prospect of being confined in them. In those of them which I have visited, I have observed several pale and dejected persons, and many fresh graves." (Howard, 1791).

Howard's writings suggested that the sick or suspect body was excluded from the 'healthy' society, rather than properly treated and taken care of. Lazarettos were liminal spaces located between a town and the rest of the world, between health and sickness, between life and death. The liminality of these spaces is apparent in their location and architecture.

Most lazarettos were strategically located far enough, not to threaten the city's safety, but close enough to remain under administrative control. Lazarettos were designed with strict boundaries that secured their total isolation from the rest of society. Those strict boundaries multiplied within them. Their basic morphology consisted of a series of rooms arranged in a square around a central courtyard that allowed the proper airing of the rooms and protection from the rain. In their interiors, most of these structures contained separate spaces for the confinement of passengers, animals, personal possessions and merchandise. The space was designed to secure the submission of the quarantined subjects. Their rooms were arranged in such a way that the inmates were not able to get in touch with each other. In strategic points of the complex, as at the end of each row of rooms, there were towers, from which the guards and the commander could watch and inspect the whole lazaretto area. In some cases, these towers were built in the building's corners allowing the inspection not only of the interior but also of the exterior of the building. The commander usually resided in the upper rooms. The residences for the lazaretto's personnel, the head doctor, the nurses, and the guards, were often located a bit further from its main area and none of them were allowed to have any contact with the town. Apart from the rooms, the complex could include a small hospital unit, a chapel with burying ground, a prison for the offenders, and infrastructure for cleansing. The kitchen and storage rooms were located far from the confinement rooms, and there could exist a small recreation area, a garden and a reception room where the 'clean' could meet their visitors by keeping a distance through railings and grids, which was known as *parlatorio* or *parlor*.

Many lazarettos followed the logic of the fortress architecture, especially those built on remote islands across the ports and the cities. Precisely the lazaretto of Aegina (36 km or 23 mi from Athens) was built in a unique amphitheatrical arrangement reminiscent of Jeremy Bentham's conception of the *Panopticon* in the 18th century. Bentham gave shape to a ubiquitous system of prison surveillance, offering ultimate power to the guards based on visibility. Prisoners were being seen but could not see. Incarcerated in their cells, all looking towards the central tower —as the building was cylindrical—they were exposed to the guard and hidden from the rest of the inmates. Invisibility guarantees order and visibility guarantees discipline, or rather self-discipline. Surveillance was, therefore, the main system put in practice by the architectural and spatial apparatus that constantly inscribed in the exposed bodies a non-personal and non-physical power relation.

This visibility trap was put in practice in many lazarettos, built perimetrically, around a court, thus giving the guards and the commander a bird's-eye view on the inmates' activity. Care and empathy are absent from the testimonies and the descriptions of these spaces. It seems like the management was rationally planned, aiming to ensure the effectiveness of the measures at the highest speed possible. The lazaretto was at the same time a space for sanitary prevention and a disciplinary mechanism, responding to all the details defined by the quarantine laws and penal rules.

The seeping of administration in architecture was implemented through spatial techniques that regulated the inmates' movement through carefully planned routes, which defined the precise use and access to each space. It provided multiple levels of inspection with towers and second storeys. Space in lazarettos was managed similarly to other institutional buildings (prisons, asylums, schools, factories). Precisely because of their size and structure, many lazarettos were, in the years that followed, hosting refugees, or were turned into prisons, mental asylums and concentration camps.

The Lazaretto at Syros, 19th century

From the 14th until the 19th century, quarantine was often inherent to traveling. Sailors, traders, scientists, doctors, artists, archaeologists, pilgrims, escapists, opportunists, vagabonds, criminals, and 'tourists' of the time, all kinds of maritime travelers and a multitude of different people were kept in quarantine inside the lazarettos to undergo health control before entering new territories.

However, the most frequent travels were the commercial ones; especially with the spread of colonization, the movement of people and goods was happening at a larger scale. Since the steam engine and the railway development were still in their early stages, transportation was mainly taking place by the sea. But as said, maritime travel carried along with it the danger of the spread of the disease. A transnational communication, aiming at the confrontation of epidemics spreading along the commercial sea routes, was established through the Vienna Conference in 1815. It resulted from the insistence of the great European powers, mostly France, England, and Austria, on a more accurate application of disinfection methods to secure maritime trade.

The perception of Plague changed gradually, internationally. Instead of its menacing, powerful, and fatal character, the emphasis was placed on it being an obstacle to maritime commerce that had to be overcome. During the reforms of the sanitary regime in Europe, the commercial and medical

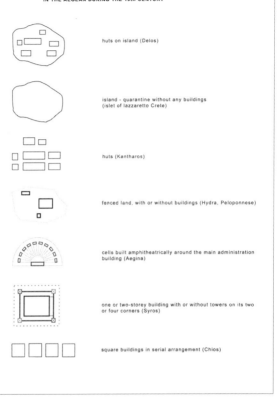

ARCHITECTURAL TYPOLOGIES FOR THE QUARANTINE STATIONS
IN THE AEGEAN DURING THE 19th CENTURY

huts on island (Delos)

island - quarantine without any buildings
(islet of lazzaretto Crete)

huts (Kantharos)

fenced land, with or without buildings (Hydra, Peloponnese)

cells built amphitheatrically around the main administration
building (Aegina)

one or two-storey building with or without towers on its two
or four corners (Syros)

square buildings in serial arrangement (Chios)

Fig. 19
Architectural typologies of lazarettos
in Greece, 19th century.

world was concerned with the long quarantine duration in the ports of the Western Mediterranean (Malta, Marseille, Trieste). The high costs of the quarantine undermined the time gained by the invention of the steamboat. As part of the European health reforms, many scientific missions sponsored by the great European powers were sent to the Eastern Mediterranean to inquire about the health regulations and trade relations on a nosological, administrational, and financial level. The knowledge of each country's port system allowed the European governments to avoid mistakes in their sanitary reforms. The 'proper' quarantine in the East was the foundation for any sanitary reform in the West. Soon it was believed that a deep and meticulous object cleansing was more important than long-term confinement. For this was needed to construct well-functioning and sustainable lazarettos, and to ensure the good application of prevention measures, rules and regulations.

The Transformation of the Lazaretto at Syros

The relationship between health and financial management and the interference of the European powers in the Eastern Mediterranean can be well understood in the development of the sanitary system in Greece. More precisely, in the example of the lazaretto at Syros. After its independence from the Ottoman Empire, the newly formed Greek state made a decisive turn to the West. The Aegean ports became the first European stations for ships coming from Asia and Africa. Understanding the importance of its strategic location, Greece, under the European influence, gradually organized its sanitary system to protect its borders—and consequently, the European borders—from highly contagious diseases carried along with maritime commerce. The first attempts for the institution of a defensive port system were made during the Temporary Administration (1822–1827), under the Ministry of the Navy's instructions. Although there was some quarantine infrastructure already put in place during the Ottoman Era, the sanitary system was planned from the start and led to new structures for sanitary control. The measures for Plague prevention escalated to their most elaborate version, the new *Sanitary Code* that was established in 1845 and included records of the sanitary regulations and decrees of the previous years. The French medical science and legislation widely influenced it. The new *Sanitary Code* reformed the agenda on quarantine and provided a complete institutional framework for sanitary policy.

Following the Greek sanitary system's development, the transformation of Syros' quarantine infrastructure can be summarized in three periods. During the Independence War in Greece and the first attempts for the application of sanitary regulations, the lazaretto at Syros changed locations, around several small and remote islets around Ermoupolis, the island's capital, such as St. Nicolas and Nisaki. The quarantine structures on these islands had the form of huts made of wood. Their shabby condition made the travelers' stay unbearable and unsafe. Consequently, a simple structure that functioned as a lazaretto was built close to Ermoupolis port, probably where the shipyard stands now. However, it did not prove to be efficient at providing adequate and safe distances for the quarantined people, and several islets kept being recruited for quarantine. Several testimonies, from various sources, confirm the bad condition of the lazaretto at Syros, and at the same time, highlight the European (most often the British) involvement and mobility in the region. *Murray's Handbook*, an essential guide for travelers, included in its pages recommendations and evaluations of lazarettos. Murray's first *Red Book*, published in 1836, mentions that "Hydra has one of the best Lazarettos in Greece. (...) The Lazaretto at Aegina is also good. (...) and provisions were much cheaper than at Hydra. The Lazaretto at Syra is abominable and ought by all means to be avoided." John Carne, traveler and artist, while being quarantined in Syros, wrote in his diary in 1837: "The most wretched of the houses of Syra would have been perfect comfort compared to the interior of the lazaretto, which is a disgrace to Syra, and a disgrace to England in permitting it to exist even a day longer. The walls rested on the naked rock: the floors were of rock, only a boarding raised in one part, four feet (approximately 120 cm) above the floor, and on this, the beds were laid: the rats ran in and out by dozens; the whole place swarmed with them; and everything, provisions, clothes, sketches, were slung up to the roof for safety from their inroads. When it rained it poured without mercy: the inmates were half-drowned." Dr. John Bowring, a doctor appointed by the British Government during his mission in the Levant, confirmed and warned that travelers in quarantine could be subjected to other dangers and diseases, even die, because of the unsustainable conditions in some quarantine stations. After visiting Syros, he wrote: "In the *Lazzaret at Syra* where the exactions are monstrous, and where lately there was not even a water-proof roof to shelter the invalid, I have seen a person come out of his imprisonment having had his garments devoured by rats, and his person disfigured by multitudinous vermin."

As Ermoupolis was growing to be an important commercial port with increased maritime traffic and according to European researchers' suggestions, the need for a new lazaretto in Syros became urgent. Discussions on the new lazaretto had already started in 1834, but the construction was probably delayed due to its overestimated cost. Finally, the new lazaretto at Syros, designed according to European standards by the Bavarian architect Wilhelm von Weiler, began in 1839 and was completed in 1841. It was indeed a costly and architecturally impressive building. The new *Murray's Handbook*, published in August 1840, includes it as "one of the best in the Levant", and recommends it in 1854: "It will be useful [for travelers] to remember that the best Lazarettos in the Levant are those of Syra, Piraeus, Corfu, and Malta."

Categorizing Danger

The 1845 *Sanitary Code* in Greece set several categorizations according to the places of origin of humans, animals and merchandise, which would define each vessel's sanitary treatment reaching a port. Fundamental was the distinction of places between sanitary immune and non-sanitary immune, which in their turn were divided into clean, suspect and unclean. Those coming from non-sanitary immune places had to undergo the cleansing process. The confinement duration and the cleansing period were defined by the authorities and depended on the estimation of the danger for public health. In general, an average duration before 1845 was about 7 days for humans and 15 for merchandise. The 1845 *Sanitary Code* defined the confinement and cleansing time more precisely. The contaminated merchandise could remain in the lazarettos for up to 4 weeks, in order to be fully disinfected.

The same distinctions were made for arriving ships and humans: free / clean / suspect / unclean / contaminated. The harbors were also divided into categories according to their infrastructure and commercial relations. Some were obliged to cease communication with all ships from any country; some could accept only free ships. Some could accept free, clean and suspect ships, and very few could accept all ships.

Cleansing Methods

The cleansing methods applied to secure the transition from quarantine to free communion may remind rites of passage. In case there was no contamination, the confined passengers were allowed to move freely again. However, cleansing was a costly process, taken into account in the travel expenses. The Greek lazarettos fostered the cleansing methods already used in Europe: *sorino* (after 1832), and *spoglio* (after 1836). During sorino the ship and its crew stayed for a short period isolated and immobile close to the port until there was an estimation of their health condition. At the same time, the merchandise was taken to the lazaretto for precautionary cleansing. Spoglio demanded that persons judged by the sorino as suspect or contaminated had to enter the lazaretto. They were stripped and washed with hot water (28°–30° Réaumur) for at least 15 minutes. They had to get dressed in new clothes, bought on their own expenses from the local town. The old clothes got fumigated and aired for several days.

Some details on the cleansing of specific goods in the old lazaretto of Syros can be found in the minutes of the first Sanitary Commission of Syros, that was held on the 13th of August, 1832:

During the first years of the function of lazaretto at Syros, the confined passengers, inspected by the guards, had to wash their clothes and possessions, by dipping them inside the sea for 3 hours. They had to repeat the process 2 or 3 times per day. Precious or sensitive objects and clothes were aired inside the confinement huts during the daytime and in plain air during the night. Merchandise and personal possessions were purified by constant airing, turning, and fumigation. Certain items, though, such as cotton, straw, feathers, and, above all, paper, were considered important sources of infection that needed tenacious and more special treatment.

The top side of soaps was washed and exposed to the sun for 8 days. Threads and filaments were separated from skeins, aired, turned, and exposed to the sun for 41 days. Dry leather was exposed to the air and sun for 41 days. Raw leather preserved in salt was opened and dipped separately into the sea for 2 days. The owner had to take it out with a long stick.

Letters, books, and artists' sketches were aired and fumigated with camel manure or herbal mix and sulfur flower. Official mail and coins were disinfected using vinegar.

Outgoing letters were often slit by a blade to ensure the seeping of the sterilizing effect. Finally, they were marked by a cachet, or authorized stamp, to show that disinfection had been carried out.

Quarantine Privileges

The quality of life and the residing conditions were different in each lazaretto. Local and state regulations were administered in many different types. The confined and isolated passengers must have been in a constant emotional struggle under the heavy shadow of death. That may be apparent by their notes and engravings on the institutional walls. However, most testimonies offer information on the details and practicalities of the stay in the lazaretto. There are many descriptions of the discomfort and awful conditions in many of them. Test-imonies talk of frozen, empty cells made of stone that were inhospitable. Others report the lack of strict measure compliance that could ruin the quarantine's effectiveness, or incidents of financial exploitation. Confinement in shabby infrastructures could sometimes be paid highly for what it offered. Many travelers experienced their stay in lazarettos as a compulsory and unpleasant interruption in their professional or leisure trip, as "imprisonment with the chance of catching the Plague" and "a serious drawback to the pleasures of an Eastern tour." However, some contemporary travel guides and testimonies suggested the opposite. They presented it as a productive and peaceful time of reflection. A *New Guide to the Levant* suggested in 1840 that "should you be thinking of perpetrating a book or to write up your journal there is no place equal to the lazaretto. By thus rationally employing yourself, instead of grumbling at necessary confinement, each succeeding day will bring with it fresh pleasure, rendered still more acceptable from the conviction that it has not been time entirely thrown away."

Travel goes hand in hand with financial and industrial development. Therefore citizens from industrially advanced countries that had an advantage in mobility, cultural and scientific trips, and communication were the most frequent travelers. Many of the written testimonies saved during the 19th century from the lazaretto of Syros were by English travelers, whose mail demonstrates their privilege over the other inmates and represents only part of the life in the lazaretto. Class distinctions were applied. In the new lazaretto at Syros, the wealthier passengers enjoyed better conditions, as they could pay for having better quality furniture, food orders, and amenities during their stay, as they were accommodated in separate, more luxurious, and spacious rooms. The following excerpts from diaries and letters written by passengers confined in the new lazaretto at Syros highlight some aspects of their experience of such a place.

On his travel from Turkey to Athens, Charles Fellows (1799–1860), a wealthy and influential Englishman, traveler and archaeologist, passed his quarantine in the new lazaretto of Syros in 1840. In a letter to his publisher John Murray jr he wrote: "Quarantine and the existence of a regular post, mark the verge of our European world. (…) our detention is but 14 days here, and probably only a day or two at Trieste. I believe none of our party would have regretted it had it been longer, for we have much occupation in threshing out the corn of our late abundant harvest." His young assistant, illustrator, and art critic, George Scharf jr (1820-95), in another letter described their room and the conditions of their stay: "The apartments are a series of low rooms with a door, windows, and chimney, about twelve in a row, each door numbered and turned in various directions. Fortunately, we had a very comfortable one assigned to us with a guardian to watch us and keep us from touching other people. Without him, we are tied or locked in our room."

A testimony by another traveler, George Ferguson Bowen, sets more broadly these differences. In September of 1847, he wrote in his diary: "After dinner, at about 5 o'clock, I was rowed to the Lazaretto, where I was installed in 3 tolerably comfortable rooms for which I was to pay 3 drachmas or 2 shillings a day. The suite of rooms next to me is occupied by two Greek merchants settled at Malta who are very civil and obliging fellows. I am the only Englishman and, except for the above, the only person with any claim to gentleman designation. (…) Also, during the day, we have a bit of rocky shore to expatiate on, and I mean to take a delicious plunge in the sea every morning. Our meals are very fairly furnished from a hotel attached to the Lazaretto—which also has supplied me with two rickety deal tables, a truckle bed, a basin and jug and 2 straw-bottomed chairs. My rooms are in rather a dilapidated state. Otherwise, they are comfortable enough, and they command an excellent view of the harbor and towns. (...) I have also amused myself reading the inscriptions which former tenants have left on my walls, many of them very like those found in regular prisons. One man has made a calendar of his week's confinement and seems to have rejoiced greatly in scratching out day after day. (...) Incarcerated along with us; however, 50 or 60 Levantines are divided off inwards just like those of a prison, with each ward having its guardiano. Nearly everyone carries a stick, chiefly to keep away those not in the same quarantine as himself. For exercise, we have a court, round which the wards are situated on 3 sides and on the 4th, the double-railed space where strangers come and gaze at us walking up and down like caged wild beasts."

Discipline and Punish

This last quotation demonstrates except for the difference in class and stay quality, the severeness of surveillance. The preciseness that outlined everyday life in lazarettos in Greece had to be preserved at any cost. Until the *Sanitary Code's* consolidation in 1845, there was constant communication and collaboration among local authorities, guards, and doctors that secured everyone's compliance with the quarantine regulations, that were in a constant process of definition. It is striking that the committees regulating the function of the lazarettos usually consisted of one doctor while the rest of the personnel were mainly guards and administrators.

The location, the spatial arrangement, and the architecture made sure that travelers in quarantine were isolated from the port and the city. Still, their further isolation inside their rooms was secured by strict legislation and surveillance. The *Sanitary Code* established the management of the epidemic through policing. It comprised two parts, the Administration and the Penal. The Administration contained all the regulations concerning the proper function of the lazarettos and the smaller sanitary structures. At the same time, the Penal described the strict penalties imposed on all sorts of sanitary infringements. In Syros, a special law assigned to a group of soldiers and policemen, under the commands of the sanitary department's director or his deputy, to safeguard the inmates' compliance with the sanitary measures, and a military boat was guarding the quarantine infrastructures. The offenders were punished with temporary or life imprisonment, even death, depending on the gravity of the offense, especially if they consciously inserted into the state any contaminated human, animal, ship, or object.

Travelers' testimonies confirm this aspect

of life inside the lazarettos at Syros around the 1840s. Sir Francis Galton wrote in 1840 that "Violation of quarantine is a grave offense. A soldier would shoot a person without mercy if that appeared to be the only way of preventing it."

Therefore, the provision and healthcare were safeguarded by decrees that incorporated and legitimized the central role of the police and the army in the name of public health. Susan Sontag observed that this military confrontation was transferred, on a linguistic level, from the confined or the contaminated person to the particle of the bacterium itself, when it was proven guilty: "The military metaphor in medicine first came into wide use in the 1880s, with the identification of bacteria as agents of disease. Bacteria were said to 'invade' or 'infiltrate.' But talk of siege and war to describe disease now has, with cancer, a striking literalness and authority. Not only is the clinical course of the disease and its medical treatment thus described, but the disease itself is conceived as the enemy on which society wages war." (Sontag, 1978). The invisible 'foreign' enemy is ever since represented as an invader that should be eliminated by force. Thus this claim of power against an invisible enemy, sometimes of unknown origin and properties, functions as a communication maneuver. It seeks to coil society in an alliance and submit it to specific orders using military rhetoric rather than the dialectics of empathy, mutual respect and love for the other.

The End of the Lazarettos

Most lazarettos remained open and functional until the mid19th century. The technological progress in medicine and commerce, which included the development of chemical disinfection methods, of hospital construction, and the spread of steam power, eventually led many lazarettos to close down. This was a slow and long process. Some of them continued to function or were recruited, even in the 20th century, in case of emergency and others were used for other purposes, often connected to confinement and discipline.

Defoe, Daniel. A Journal of the Plague Year. New York: Dover Thrift Editions, 2001.

Douglas, Mary. Purity and Danger: An Analysis of Concepts of Pollution and Taboo. London: Routledge & Kegan Paul, 1980.

Foucault, Michel. Discipline and Punish: The Birth of the Prison. New York: Vintage Books, 1995.

Howard, John. An Account of the Principal Lazarettos in Europe. London:
printed for J. Johnson, C. Dilly, and T. Cadell, 1791.

Slatter, Enid. "Illustrations from the Wellcome Institute Library. The New Lazaretto at Siros (Syra), Greece, in 1840." Medical History, 28, no.1 (1984): 73-80.

Snowden, Frank. Epidemics and Society: From the Black Death to the Present. New Haven; London: Yale University Press, 2019.

Sontag, Susan. Illness as Metaphor. New York: Farrar, Straus and Giroux, 1978.

Ηλιάδη, Ιουλία. "Τεχνολογία χώρου και πληθυσμιακή διαχείριση: από το λοιμοκαθαρτήριο στο στρατόπεδο κράτησης μεταναστών." Διπλωματική εργασία για το Δ.Π.Μ.Σ. 'Σχεδιασμός - χώρος - πολιτισμός' Σχολή Αρχιτεκτόνων Ε.Μ.Π., 2015.

Καμινάκης, Θράσος. Το λαζαρέτο της Σύρου: Το λοιμοκαθαρτήριο της Σύρου και η μαρτυρία του Ségur Dupeyron. Αθήνα: Φίλντισι, 2019.

Συριανά Γράμματα. Αφιέρωμα: Λοιμοκαθαρτήριον Σύρου. 05 (2019).

Confinement and Totalitarianism Famine in Occupied Syros
Nicolas Lakiotakis

Extracts from a Covid-19 Journal of an actor

> Chania, Crete.
> March 25, confinement day 3
> Since the government decided to shut down theatres I have been trying to fill the void, but being confined makes things tough. Compartmentalising my time for a new life in isolation I set a schedule for myself: 5 hours working on a new project; 2 hours of physical activities; 1 hour studying German; 1 hour for food provisions.

March 28, confinement day 6
I'm actually going around in circles with my schedule. It turns out that having a lot of spare time is not that easy to deal with. I find great difficulties focusing on a particular activity, especially intellectual, and spend a lot of time thinking about past events.

> April 4, confinement day 13
> Came across a copy of *La Peste* (The Plague) by Albert Camus, which I bought ages ago

in *Pêle-Mêle*, a second-hand bookstore in Brussels. It seems most relevant to the health crisis we're going through. Posted it on Facebook before starting to reread it and got 89 likes. Not bad for a post that is not a picture of myself. In *The Plague*, the bacillus of a long-forgotten disease spreads uncontrollably from rats to humans. It ends up killing half the population of the French city of Oran, a representative modern town on the Algerian coast. As the epidemic seizes Oran and the disease jumps from citizen to citizen, panic and horror spread across the town and dramatically change the citizens' everyday lives and their relation to each other. Often read as an allegory of the Nazi occupation of France, the text also suggests that these epidemics remind us that the lives we assume to be so solid and secure are actually vulnerable: we can at any time be randomly exterminated by a disease, a natural disaster, or the actions of our fellow human beings.

Island of Sikinos, Aegean Archipelago.

August 10. The confinement is over. I am on Sikinos, an island where people who spent lockdown, claim that there was no change in their everyday lives. "We live in permanent confinement, after all." The Aegean sea is indeed a natural barrier; here, there is no need to erect concrete blocks like in Camus' Oran to prevent citizens from fleeing their Plague-ridden city. On the contrary, as soon as people from the mainland and abroad who own summer houses heard about an imminent ban on the free movement, they came here to take refuge from the Plague in the Covid-free island. Locals—less than two hundred of them, and mostly aging inhabitants—received the newcomers with mixed feelings: the arrival of people that are well integrated into the local society brought some liveliness into this isolated place, but it also meant the risk of the disease infiltrating into an island with poor health infrastructure.

August 14

The government announced new restrictive measures for Paros and Mykonos since there was a significant increase in the number of Covid-19 cases there. As the spectrum of the epidemic makes a comeback, so do feelings of apprehension and anxiety among locals and visitors. I think of Camus once again. The islands of this Archipelago were not saved from the Bubonic Plague, which killed many islanders throughout the centuries. The authorities, first Venetian and from the 19th century onwards, Greek, also established rules to prevent the transmission of the disease and imposed barriers for confinement: 'liminal spaces' through which people, animals, and commodities would have to transit and isolate for various periods of time. In *The Plague*, confining a whole town seemed to be the only way to protect the rest of the French Algerian territory as well as mainland France from the spread of the disease—though I cannot help but think that cafés and restaurants remained open throughout the outbreak in Oran. In our time, isolation was deemed as the most efficient measure to combat the spread of Covid-19. But what if it is the confinement in itself that triggers a health crisis?

August 16

There are strong, gusty winds today. I can hardly see Naxos through the whitecaps. This is quite unpleasant. Islanders have an ambiguous relationship with the sea, which is sometimes loved and praised, other times loathed and cursed in their folk songs. Having spent several summers here, I can understand what they mean. The sea opens routes and communication channels with the outer world, bringing at times wealth and prosperity. Still, death and suffering also come about when its fury arises. There is also the risk of communication routes being obstructed, as it happened during World War II when the islands' oxygen supply was cut.

Ο Μεγάλος Λιμός/The Great Famine

To the Greek collective memory, the word κατοχή (katoché, meaning occupation) is synonym with deprivation and starvation. To my own childhood memory, it is also synonym with the distress of my great aunt Antoinetta whenever there were leftovers on my plate after lunch or any time she was faced with an empty store cupboard. My parents would laugh at her, saying it was the 'occupation syndrome' striking again, but despite the mockery, these were a remnants of real national trauma.

Though in 21st-century Greece it is broadly accepted that the vast majority of the population faced deprivation at some point during the triple occupation of the country by the Germans, Italians, and Bulgarians. However, the myth of the 'lucky' villagers doing better than their big-city counterparts thanks to their proximity to natural resources remains. When asked about the starvation in the Cyclades, even the most senior inhabitants of Sikinos were surprised to find out that in Syros and Mykonos, only a few nautical miles further North, the number of famine-related deaths was disproportionate to the population total, and that the Cycladic Islands had one of the highest mortality rates in Greece.

Besides their policy of plundering all the natural resources, including food reserves, the occupiers prohibited the movement of both persons and goods between the occupied zones. For instance, at the worst of the crisis, the Bulgarian authorities refused to authorize the export of cereals from their zone of control to the famine-ridden regions of the South, under German or Italian control.

Furthermore, as Greece became an occupied country, the allies imposed a naval blockade on it, allowing no imports at all: the various regions had no choice but to rely heavily on local production, and urban zones and barren islands became particularly vulnerable. Additionally, the country did not have enough corn to satisfy the demand for the local diet's most basic item, especially of the lower classes: bread. Even before the war, Greece imported large quantities of corn from Canada. Syros was clearly a food-deficit zone: it produced only 15% of the grain required for the local consumption. Overall, 60% of the island's food was imported.

All of a sudden, Syros became *The Plague*'s Oran: a prison for its inhabitants were, three or four months after the beginning of the Occupation, the 'unthinkable' happened.

The wealth of the town of Ermoupolis, capital of both Syros and the Cyclades, is still reflected today in the beautiful neoclassical architecture of its public buildings, churches, and the exquisite mansions overlooking the Aegean. It is probably safe to assume that back in 1939, just two years before the Occupation, none of its inhabitants—including the poorest members of the working class—could have imagined that acquaintances, friends, parents,

Fig. 20
In the first months after the fall of Greece (April-June 1st, 1941) and particularly during the winter of 1941-1942, the country faced its worse famine since ancient times as a result of a large scale policy of plunder of the local resources by the Axis powers, the blockade of Greece by the Allies and the emergence of a solid black market. This resulted in a death toll of over 100 000 civilians.

cousins, or spouses would have starved to death.

And yet hunger seized the island of Syros just as the disease assaulted the town of Oran, whose self-confident citizens also believed the Plague was something that belonged to another age. "C'est impossible, tout le monde sait qu'elle a disparu de l'Occident" (It is impossible it should be the Plague, everyone knows it has vanished from the West, says one character). An inhabitant of Ermoupolis could have uttered the same phrase, using the word 'famine' instead of 'Plague'.

Fig. 20

Indeed, the news concerning the first victims of starvation, in September 1941, was discussed in a whispery voice among local doctors, who wouldn't dare pronounce the word famine. The Italian medical officer, Captain Manfrini—in a similar role as Docteur Rieux, the narrator and central

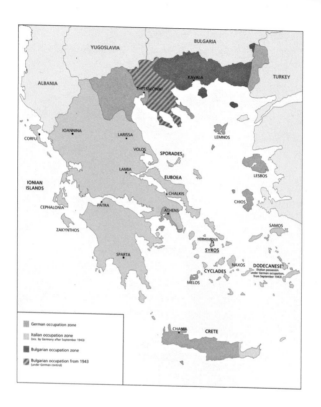

Fig. 21
The Germans, right after their victory over Greece in April 1941,
divided the country up into three zones: German, Italian and
Bulgarian. Athens and its periphery were occupied by the Germans,
the part of Northern Greece bordering Bulgaria by Bulgarians, while
most of the Cyclades, including Syros, by the Italians.

character in *The Plague*—was the first to observe and describe the disease's symptoms before eventually alerting the reluctant authorities.

Dr. Manfrini confesses that at the beginning, he also thought these were just rumors, but soon realized that things were severe and tried to talk to his superiors, who accused him of being too 'soft-hearted' towards the locals. By the time the occupation authorities acknowledged the gravity of the situation, it was too late; they were incapable of handling the health crisis.

The most severe episode of the famine in Syros lasted until May 1942. By the end of the occupation, as many as 4 000 people, out of a total population of circa 25 000, died of starvation (two more minor episodes of the hunger epidemic will occur before the end of the war). In Ermoupolis, out of about 18 000, 2 610 people starved to death.

Syros, Everyday Life in a Moribund Society

As elsewhere in occupied Greece, there was a total lack of fuel. Walking was the only means of transportation. For city dwellers, walking was indispensable to go to the farms and barter personal belongings of value for any available food or pick up edible wild greens and mushrooms. Walking was vital to bring firewood during the winter of 1941-1942, one of the harshest of the 20th century. Walking for several kilometers every day, possibly in silence, to conserve physical strength and energy. Here are some indicative distances between Ermoupolis and the villages of the island:

Ermoupolis – Episkopio and back, 5.8 km (3.6 mi)
Ermoupolis – Vari and back 12.2 km (7.6 mi)
Ermoupolis – San Michalis and back, 13.4 km (8.3 mi)
Ermoupolis – Galissas and back, 15.2 km (9.4 mi)
Ermoupolis – Finikas and back, 18.2 km (11.3 mi)

But as well as tiring, walking was also risky: Italian garrisons would stop civilians and sometimes beat them up in the roads that led to and from the town and seize whatever edibles they were carrying, under the excuse that private individuals were not allowed to trade in foodstuffs. Corruption was widespread, and the Italian soldiers plundering to serve their own needs was so extensive that it accounted for a sizable proportion of the island's already meager output.

Queueing. Queues became part of the urban scenery. Civil servants, lawyers, middle-class home-makers waiting in queues in front of the few remaining open stores, hoping to buy whatever foodstuff was available.

Queueing endless hours at soup kitchens for those who couldn't afford to shop, which was the case for an increasing number of the emaciated looking people.

By the end of 1941, the rations distributed for the whole island population per head each day were 150 gr (5.3 oz) of maize flour; 8.6 gr (0.3 oz) of pasta; 10 gr (0.35 oz) of sugar; 6.66 gr (0.23 oz) of cheese and 3.33 gr (0.11 oz) of coffee substitute. These quantities were largely insufficient to keep the local population alive in the long term—as admitted by the Italian commander of the island, Colonel Duca—and eventually led, from September 1941 to May 1942, to a death rate 6.5 times higher than in the previous years.

Fishing. Fishing was an important activity before the war, and fish a basic element in the islanders' diet. However, at the start of the occupation, the fishing industry was virtually non-existent. The war had devastated boats and equipment. Moreover, fishers were mobilized for war in the Albanian front (October 1940 – April 1941). Many of them never returned. In the pre-war years, fishers belonged to the most disadvantaged part of the population: fish was sold directly to the market at meager prices established after bargaining, and profits were hardly enough to make a decent living.

As the situation worsened in the autumn of 1941, the authorities believed that famine relief would come from the sea. But once again, the sector was heavily impacted by the excessive restrictive measures imposed by the occupiers. Although day fishing was allowed, the traditional night-fishing method was authorized only without lamps and within two nautical miles from the land; thus drastically reducing the volume of the catch. Every man ought to have a permit and was systematically checked by the military command, but, most importantly, bargaining was banned, so the fish was sold at artificially fixed, derisory prices. Consequently, the bulk of the catch ended up in the black market, where prices were much higher and wildly unaffordable for the poorer families in Syros.

Even for the fishers, it became almost impossible to bring fish home. Like the rest of the agricultural produce, the catch was requisitioned to be redistributed, supposedly on a fairer basis. Moreover, their activity asked for more calories when food was scarce; undernourished as they were, their physical state deteriorated rapidly, and many died during the famine.

Profile of an Agonizing Citizen

The Plague 's first victims were observed in the periphery of Oran, where the working class lived. Still, eventually, the epidemic reached the center of the city. In Syros, the first famine victims were unemployed industrial workers, exhausted soldiers returning from the front, and overworked fishers, mostly men.

Overall, adult males outnumbered females in the death toll, and 70% of those who died in the age group of 15 to 34 were men.

The causes can be physiological—larger body size, less body fat, faster metabolism, and higher protein and energy needs. Apart from biological reasons, many analysts claim that cultural and social ones are not negligible. When men, bedridden or walking with a stick, were unable to wait in the food queues, the family's survival relied solely on women, possibly giving them a strong incentive to survive. Conversely, unemployed young men were often described as depressed and listless. Indeed, in a patriarchal society where expectations from young adult men are high, losing one's status as family protector and breadwinner could be humiliating. It is thus argued that their poor psychological condition would have impacted their capacity to survive.

I just wonder if he knew…

Albert Camus wrote fiction about an epidemic that long ago disappeared from the Western world. The team of Doctor Rieux managed to combat by doing their duty silently and with modesty.

And yet, there's a warning "that the Plague bacillus never dies or disappears for good; that it can lie dormant for years and years in furniture and linen-chests; that it bides its time in bedrooms, cellars, trunks, and bookshelves; and that perhaps the day would come when, for the bane and the enlightening of men, it would rouse up its rats again and send them forth to die in a happy city."

While Camus was writing *The Plague*, on the other side of the Mediterranean actual people were starving to death by what is now known as the last famine of such intensity in the European territory.

This is a tribute to them.

Nicolas Lakiotakis, a theater actor and director, bounces between the Aegean and the Seine. His current work interrogates the ways official historiography forged collective myths.

Camus, Albert. La Peste. Paris: Gallimard, 1947.

Lecoeur, Sheila. Mussolini's Greek Island: Fascism and Italian Occupation of Syros in World War II. London: International Library of War Studies, I.B. Tauris & Co Ltd, 2015.

Hionidou, Violetta. Famine and Death in Occupied Greece, 1941-1944. Cambridge: Cambridge University Press, 2006.

Χιονίδου, Βιολέττα. Η Κατοχική Πείνα μέσα από Προφορικές Μαρτυρίες: Η Περίπτωση της Χίου, της Σύρου και της Μυκόνου. Αθήνα: Εκδόσεις Πατάκη, 2020.

Panic Room.
Waiting Room.
Island.
Hülya Ertas

It does not happen in one day. The anxiety of confinement arrives some weeks earlier than the actual confinement. Following the news from Wuhan and trying to make sense of what is yet to come is like drinking a bitter cocktail of fear and hope. The fear of death, mourning, unknown, is shaken with the hope for a responsible society that can contain the virus and stop the spread. With this bitter cocktail, caught unprepared, we are entering one of the most striking crossroads of individuality and collectivity, of daily life and ideology, of sanitation and sanity.

I recall dining at this little Vietnamese restaurant with Aslı some hours before the official announcement of a lockdown to be enforced across Belgium. We do not hug. Should we touch the menu? We do not order to share. This Thursday evening feels as weird as the last supper. The last supper shared with another person for the next three months.

And then, by March 13, the anxiety is replaced by reality. The experience of the pandemic begins to take on a spatial character. The State regulizes my life: where and how I can be, what I could be doing and with how many people.

The Panic Room

The first days and weeks of the lockdown felt like being in a *Panic Room*. It was a matter of life and death, and the priorities for survival had never been clearer. Luckily, the Panic Room was very well equipped with the necessary infrastructure: the Internet. Hooked by the news, on social media and chat groups, receiving unexpected texts from acquaintances, doing video calls with close friends and family. Both reluctantly and willingly receiving and participating in this information flow and online interaction. All of this was happening while I roamed within my flat and all the conversations were about one thing: survival. Planning my fulfilment of basic needs such as eating and sleeping well. The vicious cycle of trying to sleep or eat while your body is not tired or hungry at all, but you have to keep going.

Washing your hands. My hand, which actually belonged to my body, now becomes a public health issue. The threshold between the public and private spheres is dissolving. The idea of I versus the world and the lust for being unique in the universe doesn't seem to help solve the pandemic crisis we were in.

A new holistic understanding is necessary, yet I have to develop that in the Panic Room, physically alone, digitally invaded. Franco 'Bifo' Bernardi describes the situation as "the collapse of the planetary body" in his *Diary of the Psycho-Deflation*[1]. Thinking about the effects of the planetary body on my body and my impact on the planet, the idea of being one with the world is a relief. My body is embedded in the planetary body, yet locked in the Panic Room. The news stream is informing me of the imminent threat. And that feeling of nowness is so vivid that the prophetic texts of contemporary intellectuals seem useless, if not paranoid or overloaded with unfounded optimism.

And by the time I get used to this Panic Room, the feeling that I am faced with a matter of life or death starts to fade. I refresh the Twitter feed less frequently now. There is a slight decrease in direct communication with people since everyone is sick and tired of online interaction. Some people even say they need 'Me time,' despite the fact they have not seen anyone in real life for more than a month. But time goes on; we move on.

The Waiting Room

Now we are all in a *Waiting Room* with people we do not know. We are here, but no one actually knows why. Is it for a dentist appointment, job interview or checking in? Blank walls, a bare coffee table—lacking even the usual out-of-date magazines and an empty reception desk. Once in a while, one of us tries to strike a conversation. But we only ever talk and think about the same thing. The conversation does not go anywhere. It is as barren as the Waiting Room itself. Nothing is happening. We are only waiting without knowing what to expect. Some are demanding to leave, they want to return to normal. Anywhere but the Waiting Room is desirable. Some are proposing to decorate the Waiting Room, declaring that this is the 'new normal' and we have to adjust, that we have to be resilient. I stare at the walls and wait. I refuse to be over-productive or fit. I refuse to make life-changing decisions. The Waiting Room is not the best place for me to imagine anything other than the Waiting Room itself.

Some of us decide to leave. We do not know where we are going or what is left to see in the world. According to some of the conversations I overheard in the Waiting Room, the planet has been recovering in our absence. The collapsed planetary body is rising from her sickbed just as legal decisions have limited my own body. My scarcity is her abundance until we learn to be one. In the dullness of the Waiting Room I try to figure out how we will do it, how we will be able to occupy the same space and yet without (badly) impacting one another. I fail, in this bareness I am out of ideas and out of imagination. I leave the Waiting Room to get some fresh air.

The Island

Once out, I realize there is already a limit to my wandering. We are on an Island, surrounded by unpredictable waters. After two months, the confinement measures are eased a little bit. Brussels weather is surprisingly beautiful with blue skies and we start going for walks with Sander. These unplanned walks can be up to 5 hours long and are sometimes topped up with afternoon beers on the go. We never take public transport, and the walk has to be calculated according to the time we must return to our homes. This is our mental clinic Island. Our homes are like small spots in the building in the middle of this Island. The scale of the Island changes every time, depending on the perimeters of our walk. We can go around, we can enjoy the company of another person, yet we must always keep in mind that we have to return. There are actually two horizons: the abandoned city and the absoluteness of the home. The waters around us have already reminded us of their unpredictability with a second wave. Topped with a pinch of despair and consent, the Island seems like it will be our habitat for a while longer. The home will be absolute and the planetary body will not be physically constructed.

External decisions are made about my body that has failed to become one with the planetary body. The emotional rollercoaster with its peak in enjoying life, its downfall in being the productive and lowest point in survival; the pendulum of

over-connectedness within the walls and faraway-
ness of human heat. All have built these spaces of
confinement, from the Panic Room to the Waiting
Room to the Island.

Hülya Ertas is an architect, editor, curator, and coordinator of exhibitions from Istanbul living in Brussels.

1. Berardi, Franco, Bifo. "Diary of the Psycho-Deflation", www.versobooks.com/blogs. Accessed March 28, 2020.

Image credits

Fig. 1
Isolario di Benedetto Bordone

Fig. 2–3, 4–15
Wellcome Collection.
Attribution 4.0 International
(CC BY 4.0).

Fig. 5
J. and G. de Gregoriis

Fig. 6
George Thompson

Fig. 7
Herbert Johnson

Fig. 8
Ernest Schwarz-Lenoir

Fig. 11
Obrad Nicolitch

Fig. 14
Willey Reveley

Fig. 15
Étienne Rey

Fig. 16
William Henry Bartlett

Fig. 17
Dimitra Kondylatou

Fig. 18
Aikaterini Laskaridis
Foundation Library

Fig. 19
Drawing informed
by I. Iliade's drawings
in her MA thesis
'Τεχνολογία χώρου και
πληθυσμιακή διαχείριση:
από το λοιμοκαθαρτήριο
στο στρατόπεδο κράτησης
μεταναστών.', p. 27.

Fig. 20
Dimitris Harisiadis.
Photographic Archive
of the Benaki Museum.

Fig. 21
Nicolas Lakiotakis
Aristea Xanthoudaki